PINK FLOYD THE ENDLE

London / New Yc ... ng Kong / Tokyo

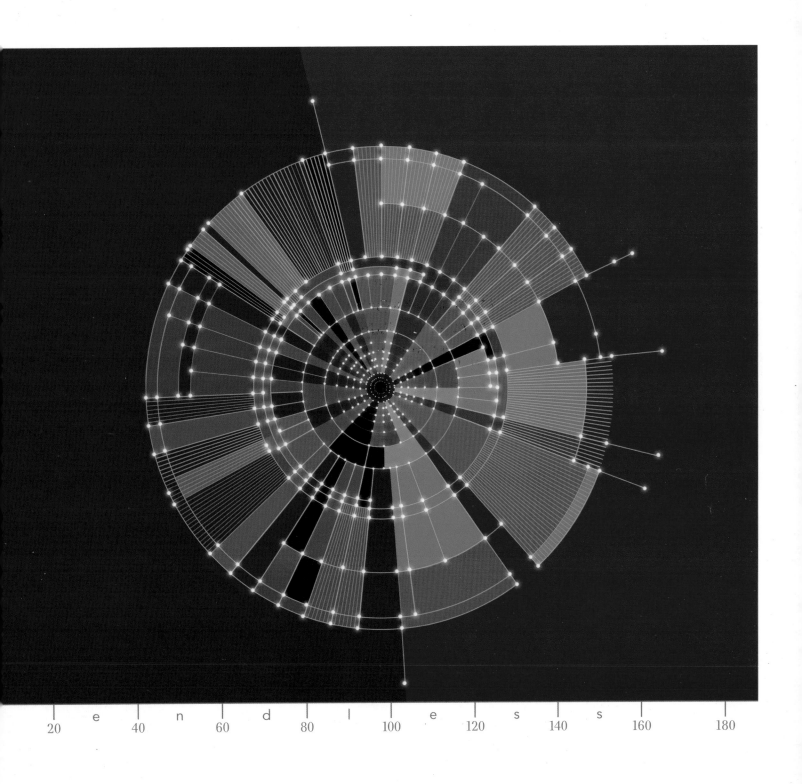

2   e   n   d   l   e   s   s

20   40   60   80   100   120   140   160   180

Published by
Wise Publications
14-15 Berners Street, London W1T 3LJ, UK

Exclusive Distributors:
Music Sales Limited
Distribution Centre, Newmarket Road,
Bury St Edmunds, Suffolk IP33 3YB, UK
Music Sales Pty Limited
Units 3-4, 17 Willfox Street, Condell Park,
NSW 2200, Australia

Order No. AM1010339
ISBN: 978-1-78305-886-0
This book © Copyright 2014 Wise Publications,
a division of Music Sales Limited

Edited by **Adrian Hopkins**
Music arranged by **Matt Cowe**
Music processed by **Paul Ewers Music Design**
Creative Director: **Aubrey Powell, Hipgnosis**
Original CD Design and Art Direction by **Stylorouge**
Original CD front cover concept by **Ahmed Emad Eldin**
Tree illustration by **StormStudios**
Photography by **Simon Fowler**

Printed in the EU

Your Guarantee of Quality:
As publishers, we strive to produce every
book to the highest commercial standards

This book has been carefully designed
to minimise awkward page turns and to
make playing from it a real pleasure

Particular care has been given to specifying
acid-free, neutral-sized paper made from pulps
which have not been elemental chlorine bleached

This pulp is from farmed sustainable forests and
was produced with special regard for the environment

Throughout, the printing and binding have been
planned to ensure a sturdy, attractive publication
which should give years of enjoyment

If your copy fails to meet our high standards,
please inform us and we will gladly replace it

www.musicsales.com

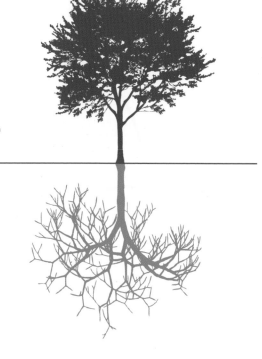

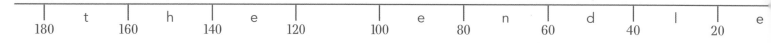

t h e e n d l e

180 160 140 120 100 80 60 40 20

s   s   r   i   v   e   r
     20   40   60   80   100   120   140   160   180

180   t   160   h   140   e   120   100   e   80   n   60   d   40   l   20   e

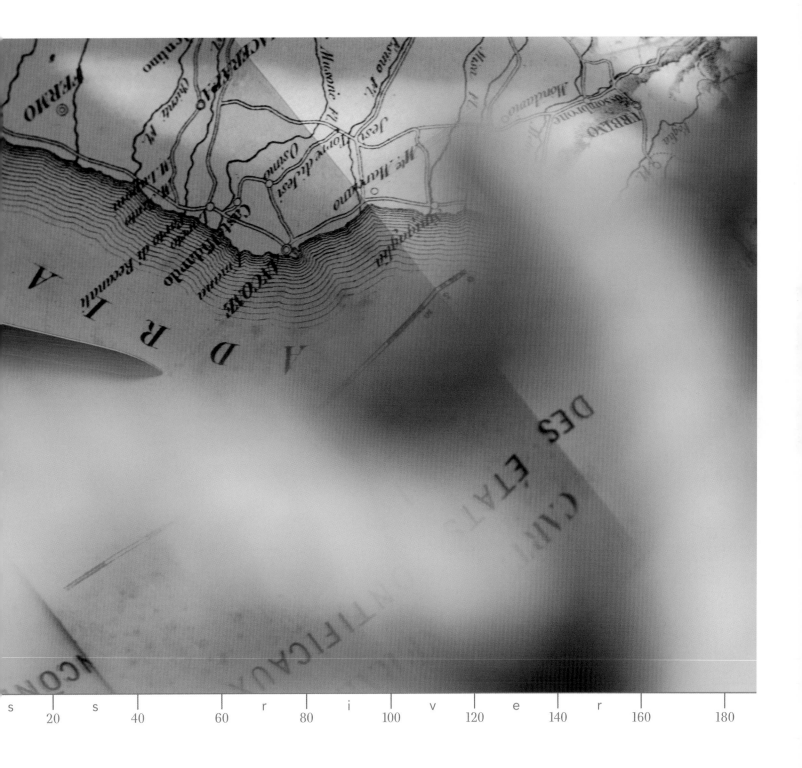

the end line

180   t   160   h   140   e   120   100   e   80   n   60   d   40   l   20   e

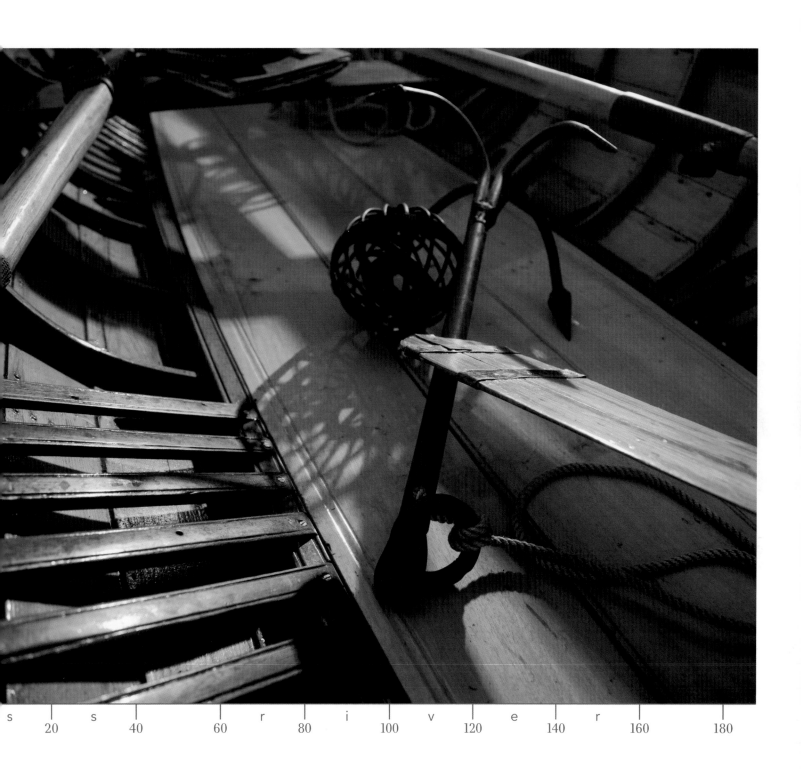

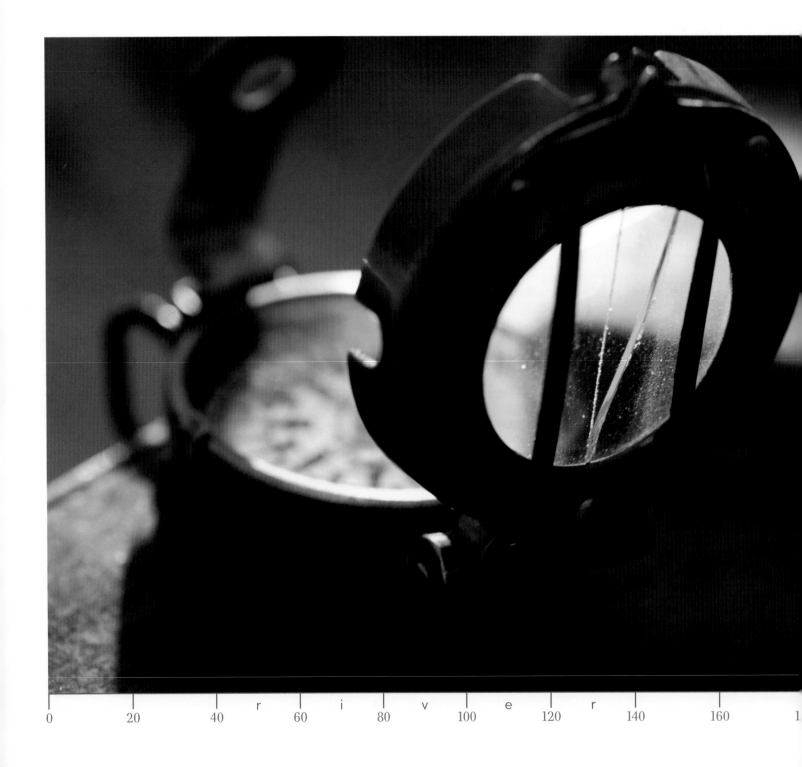

r   i   v   e   r

0   20   40   60   80   100   120   140   160

THINGS LEFT UNSAID

Music by David Gilmour & Richard Wright

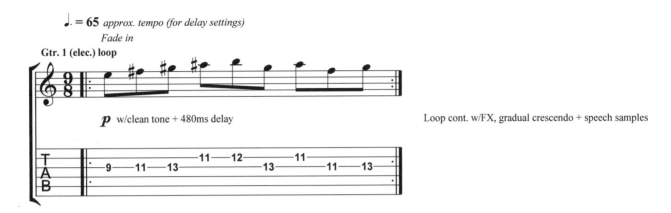

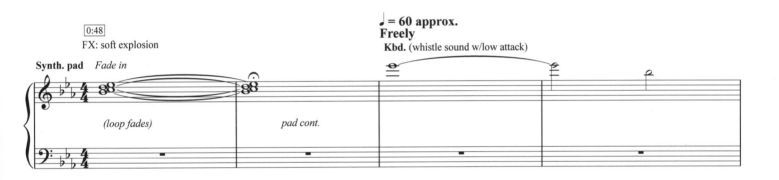

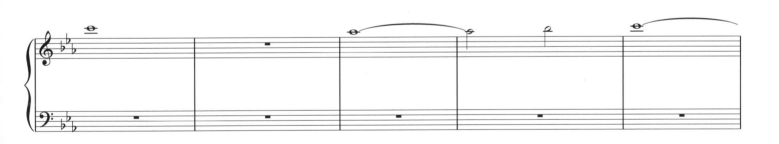

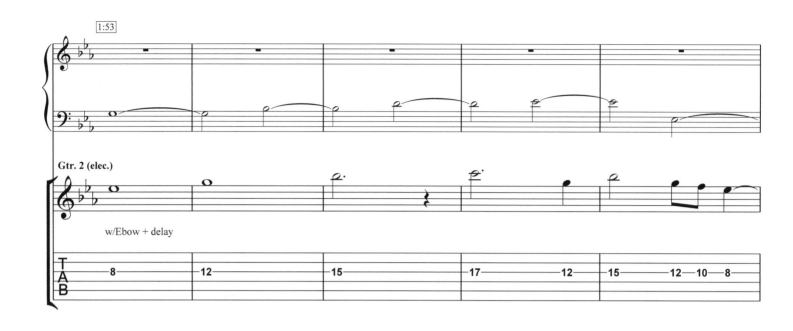

Gtr. 2 (elec.)

w/Ebow + delay

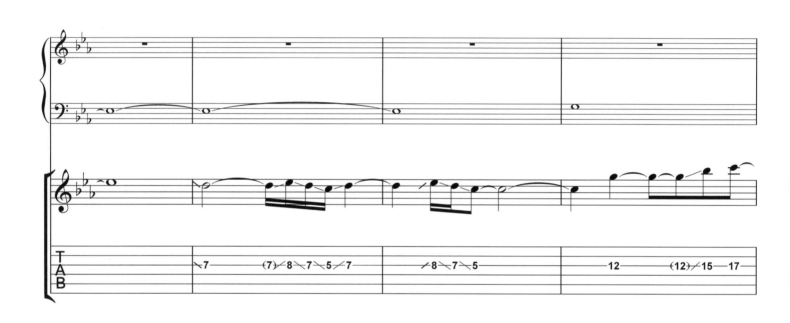

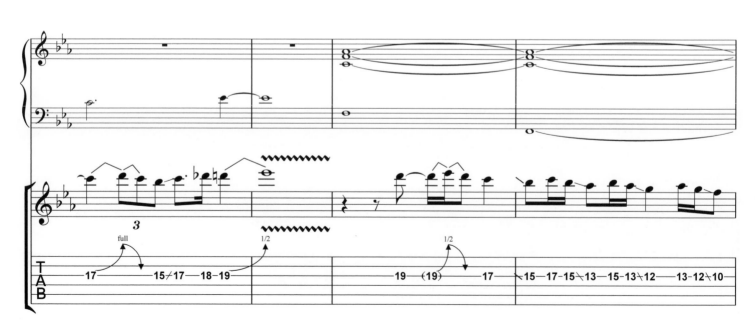

10

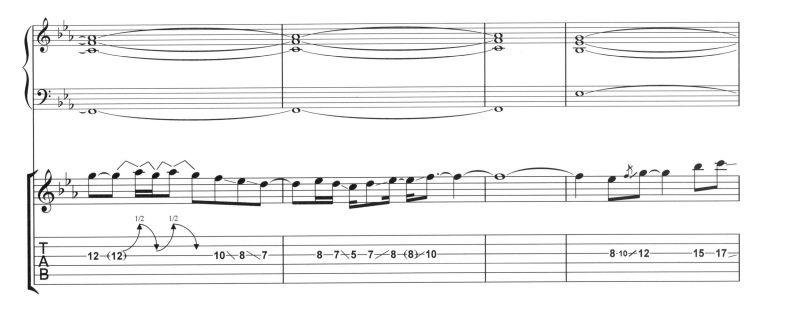

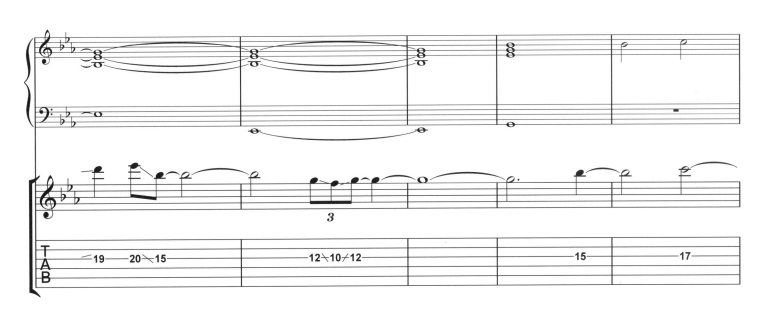

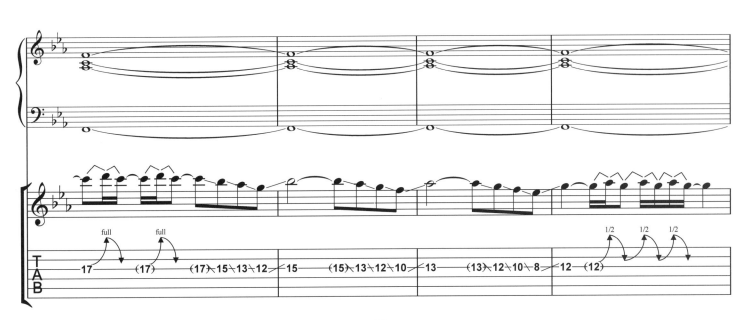

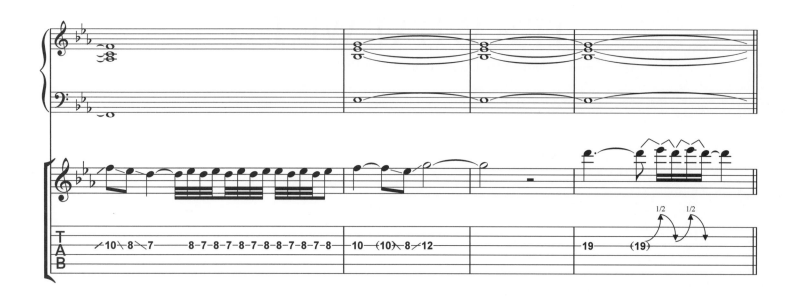

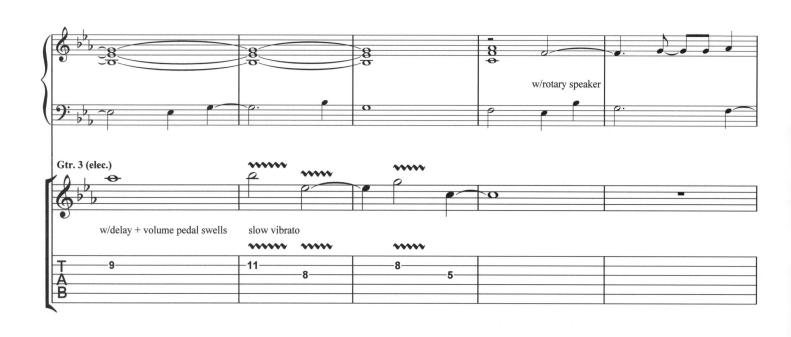

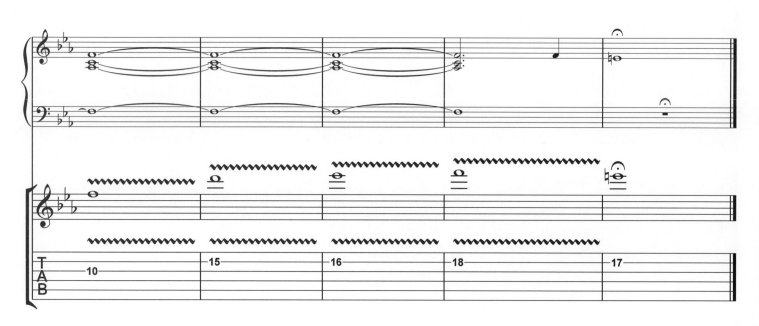

IT'S WHAT WE DO

Music by David Gilmour & Richard Wright

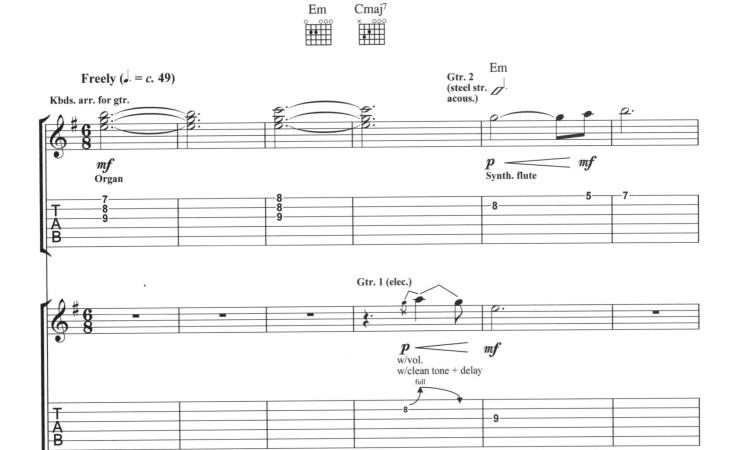

13

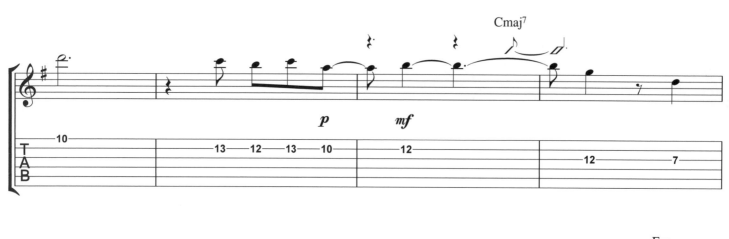

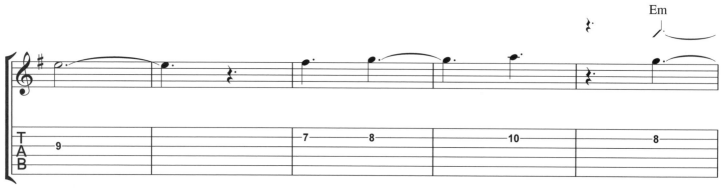

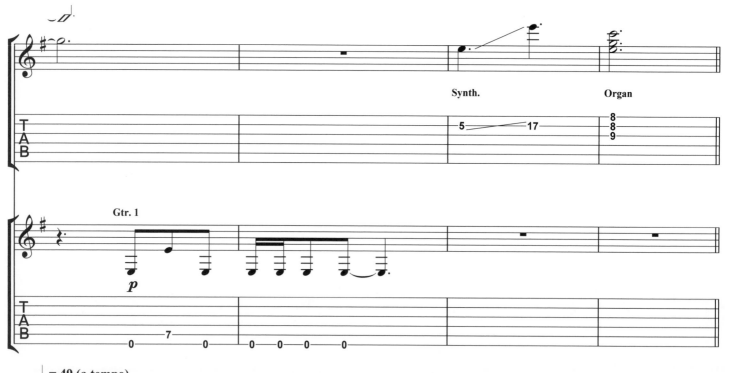

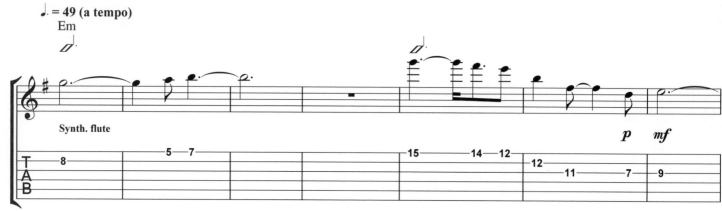

14

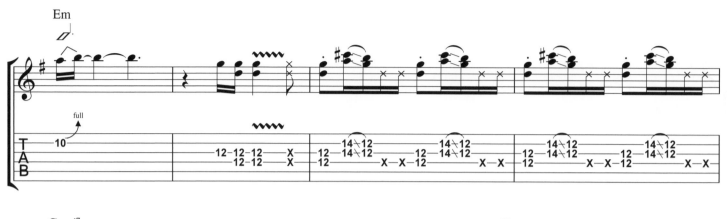

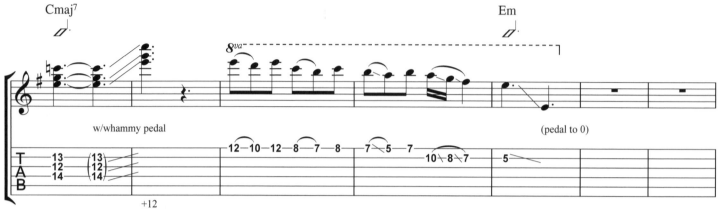

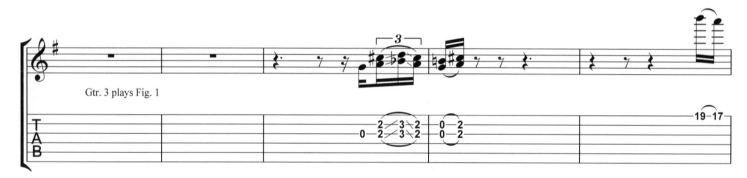

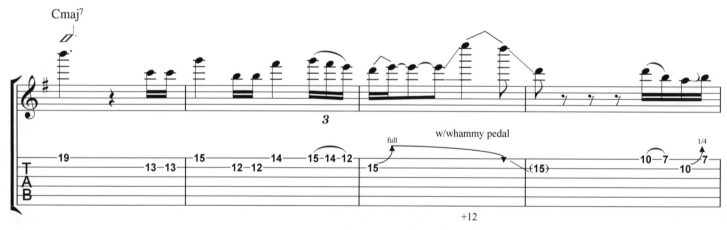

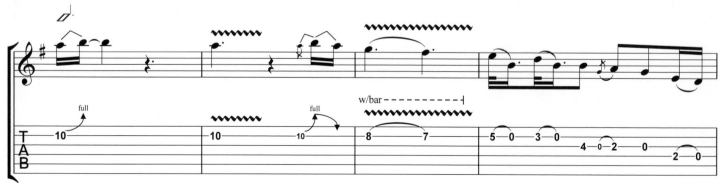

EBB AND FLOW

Music by David Gilmour & Richard Wright

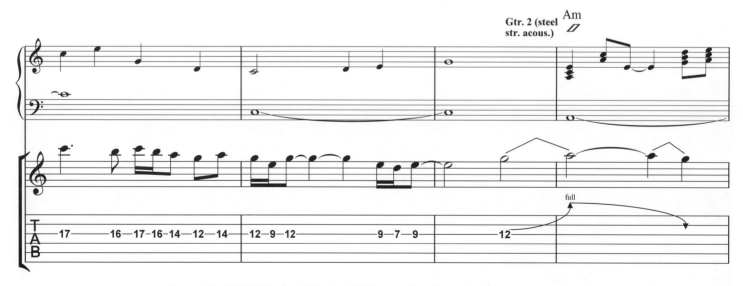

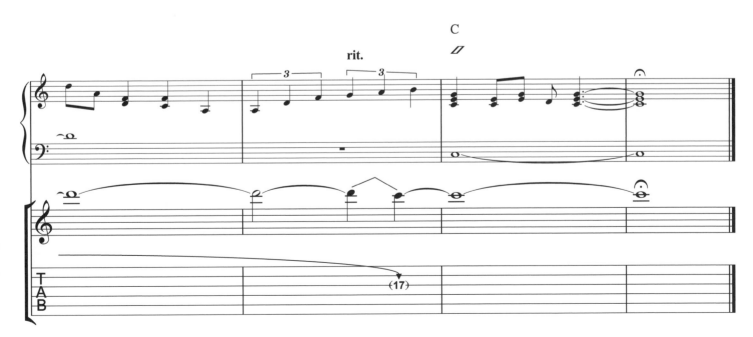

SUM

Music by David Gilmour, Nick Mason & Richard Wright

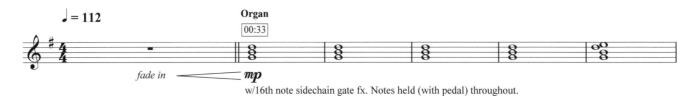

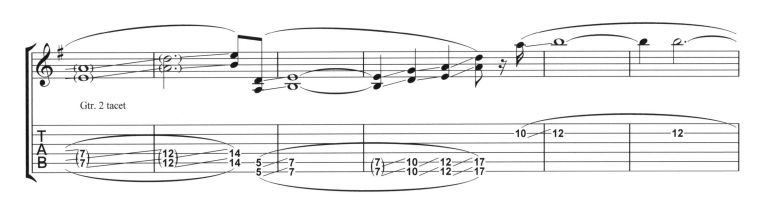

Gtr. 2 tacet

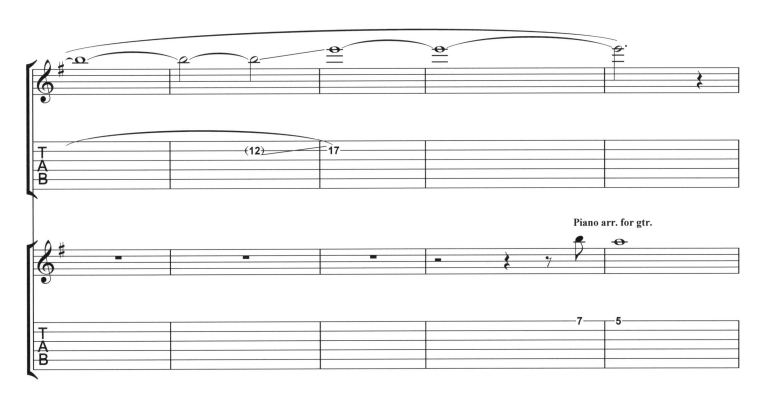

Piano arr. for gtr.

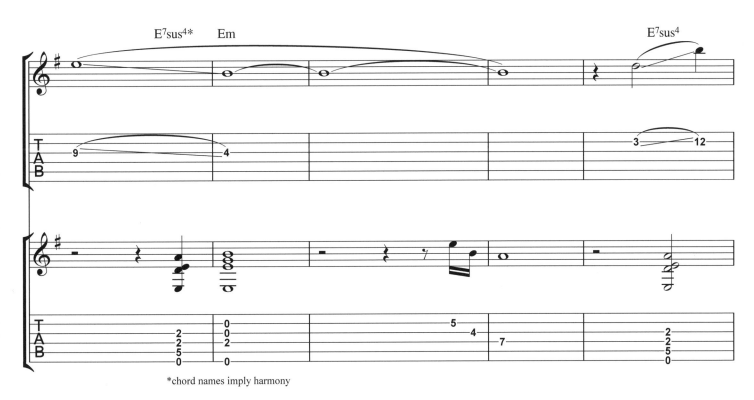

E⁷sus⁴*   Em   E⁷sus⁴

*chord names imply harmony

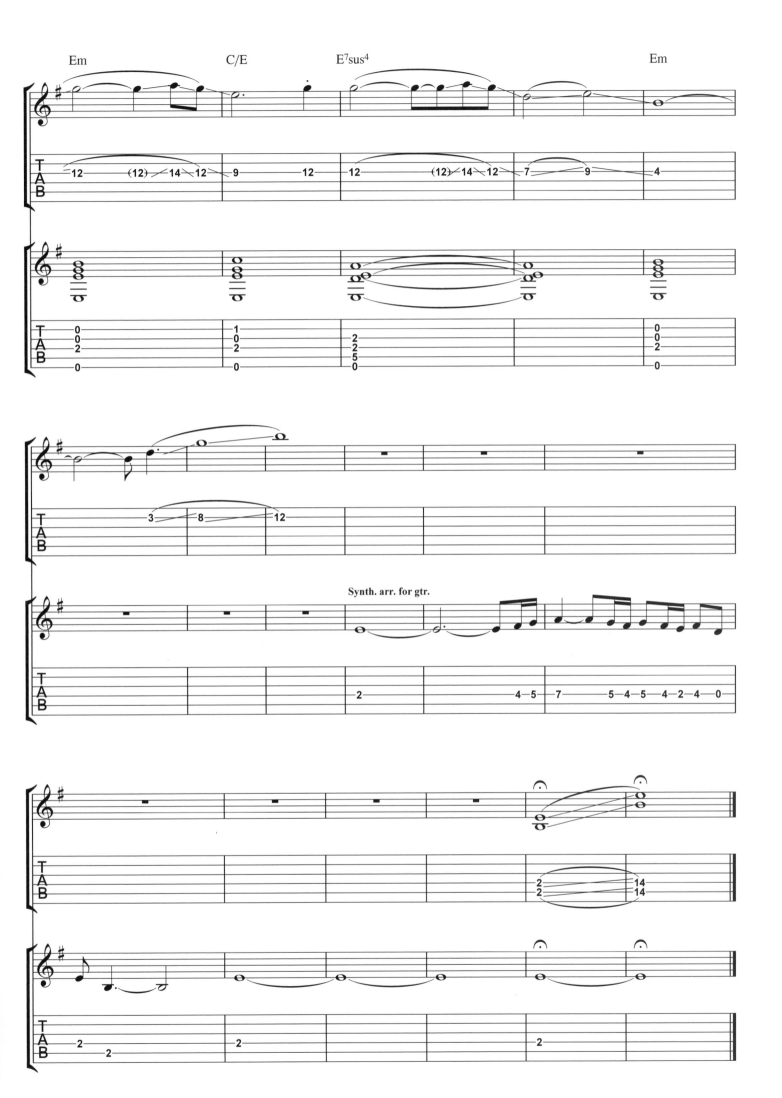

SKINS

Music by David Gilmour, Nick Mason & Richard Wright

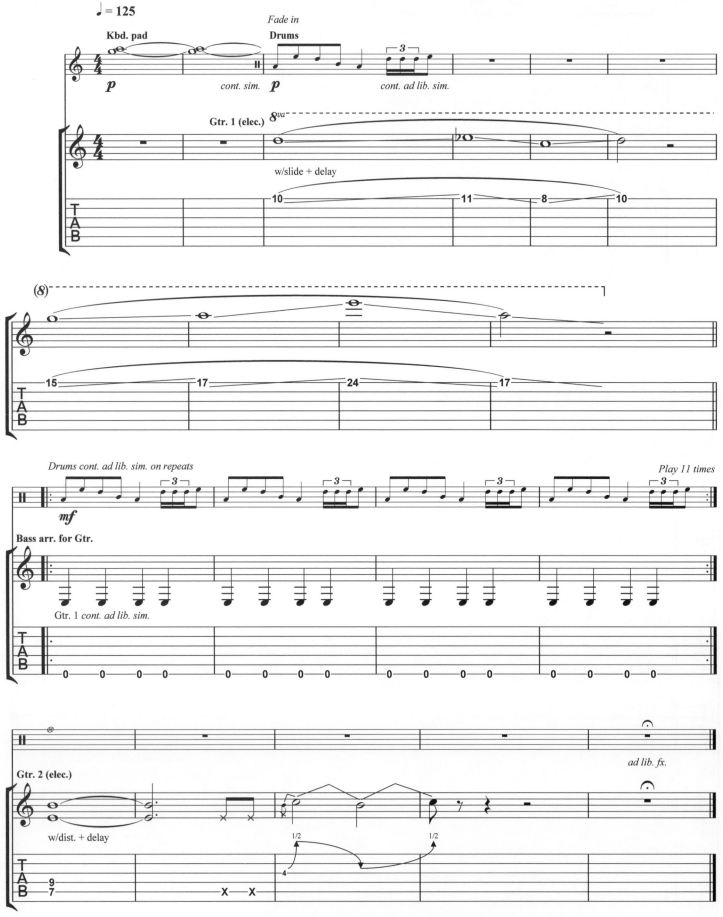

UNSUNG

Music by Richard Wright

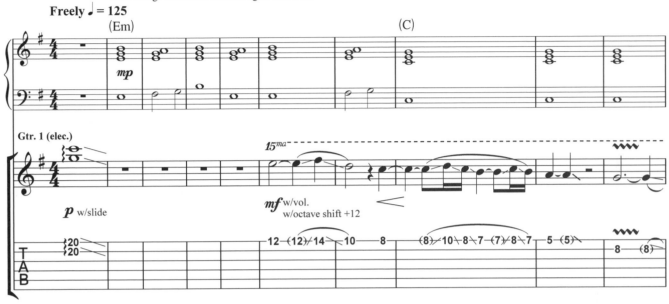

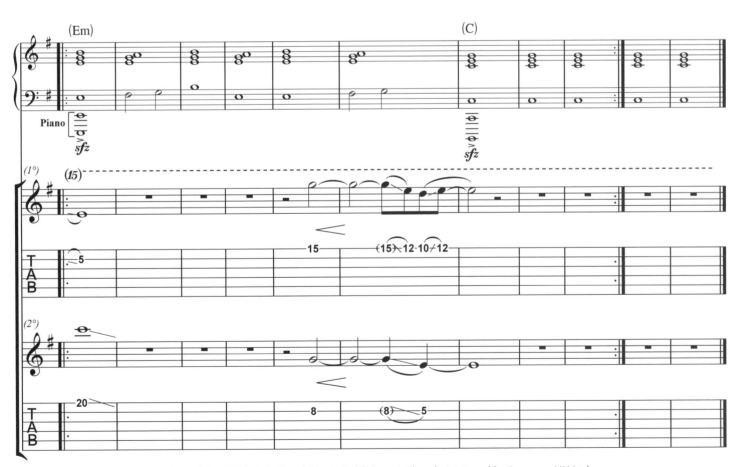

ANISINA

Music by David Gilmour

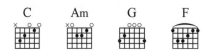

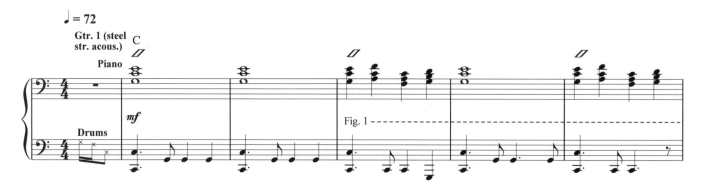

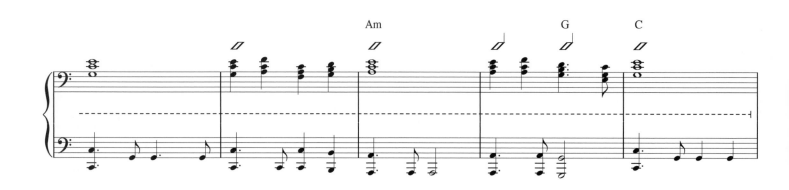

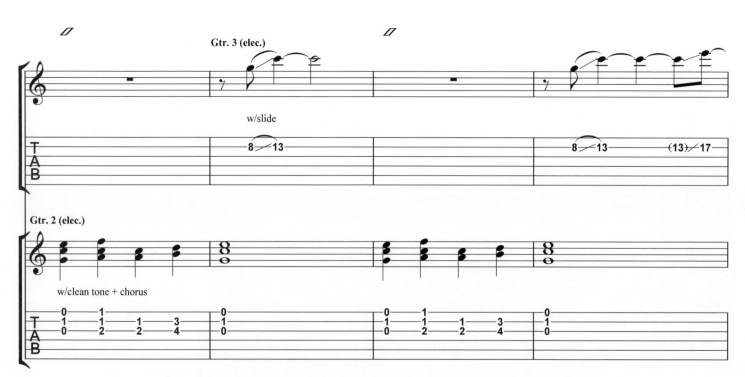

31

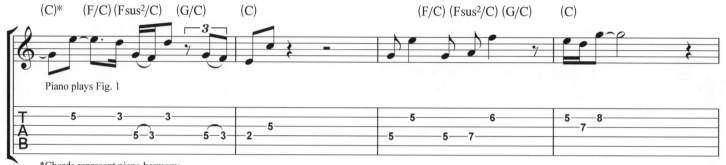

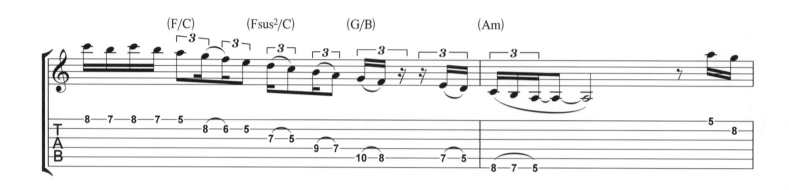

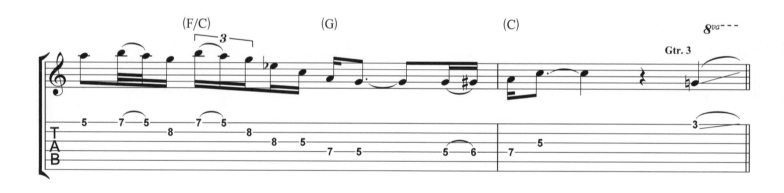

THE LOST ART OF CONVERSATION

Music by Richard Wright

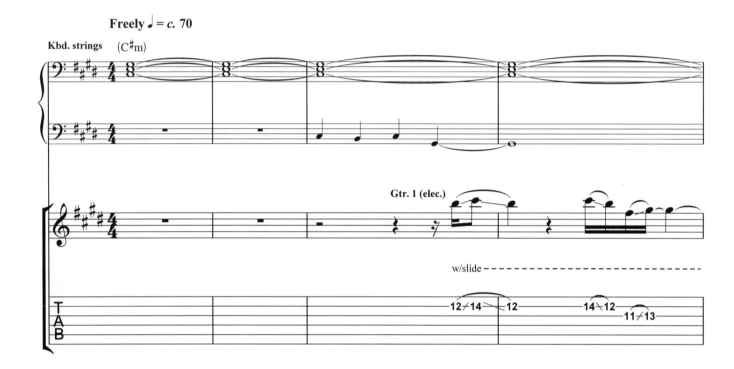

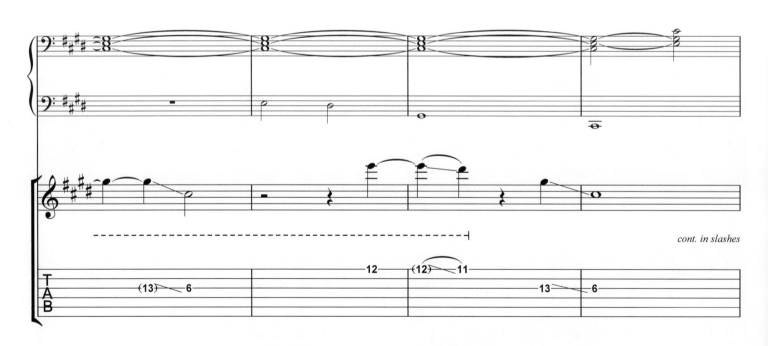

ON NOODLE STREET

Music by David Gilmour & Richard Wright

*composite part
**chords reflect overall harmony

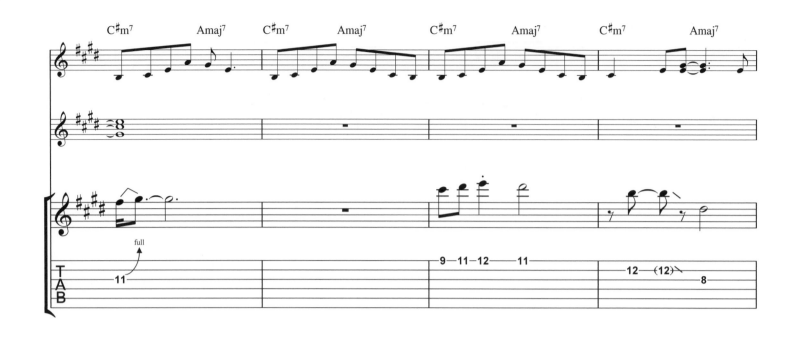

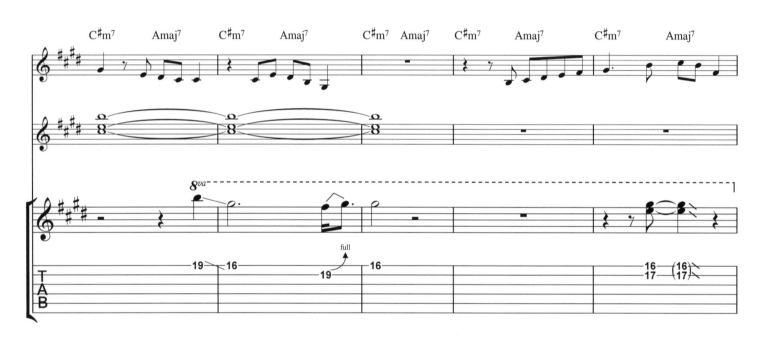

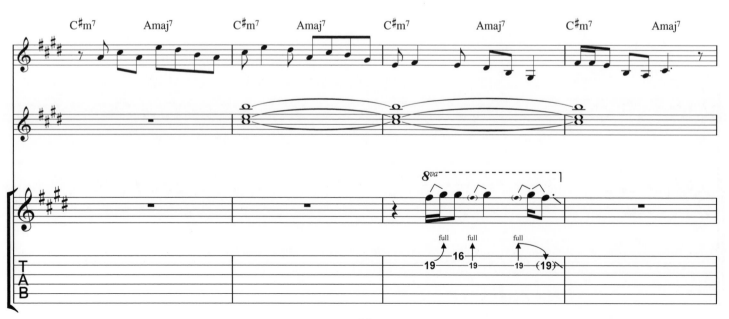

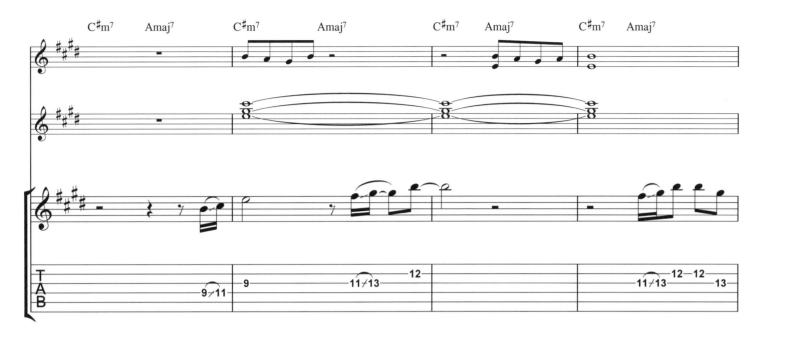

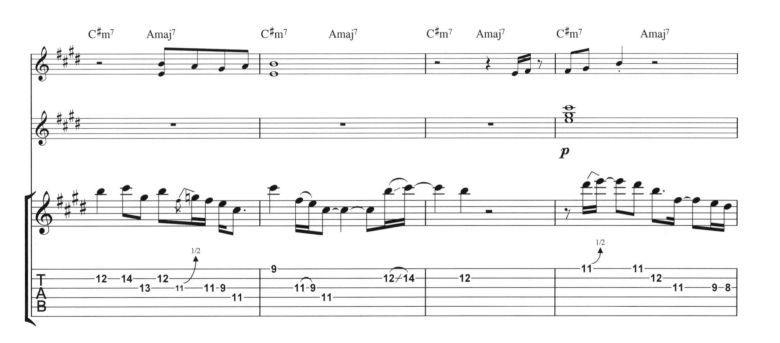

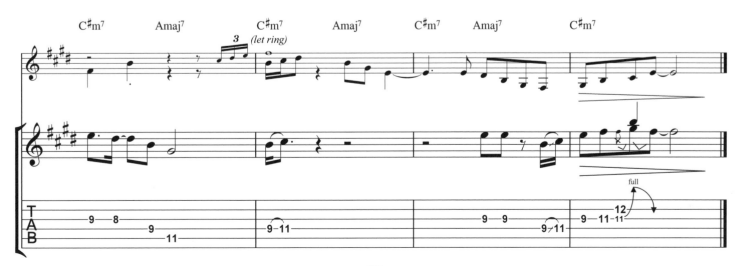

39

NIGHT LIGHT

Music by David Gilmour & Richard Wright

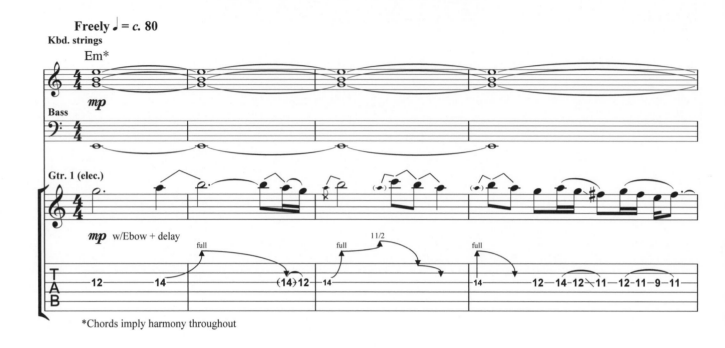

*Chords imply harmony throughout

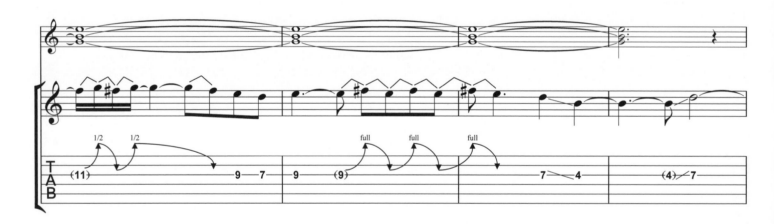

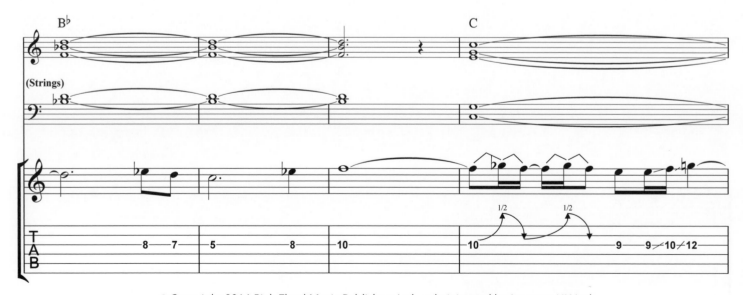

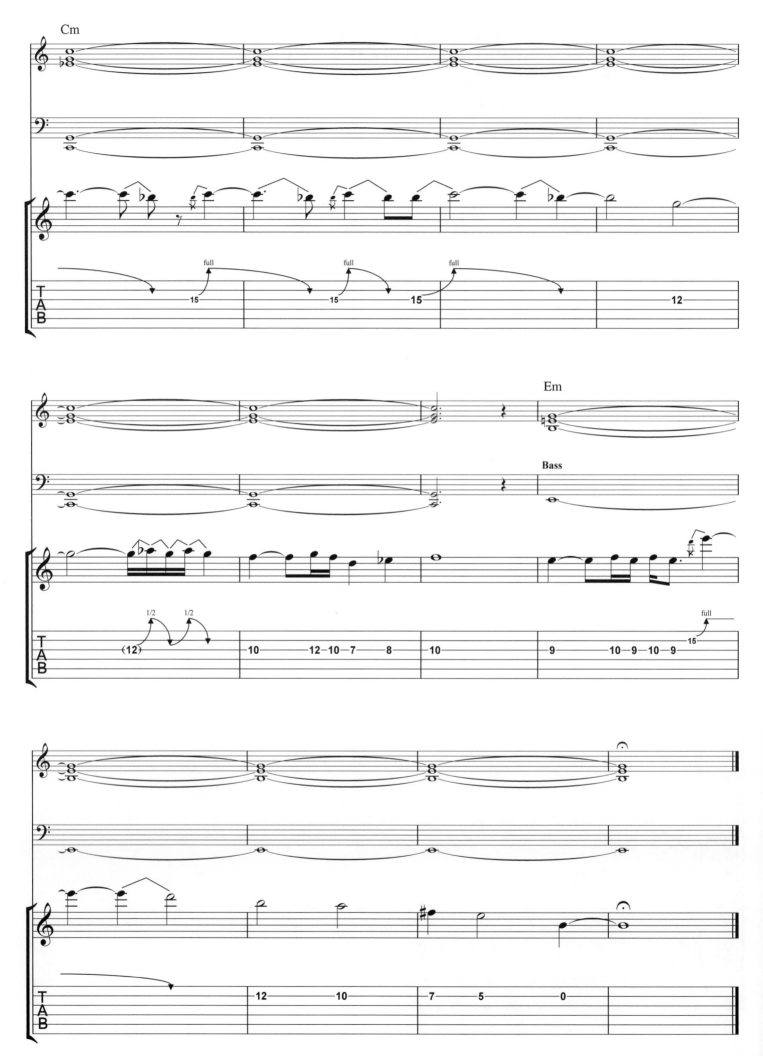

ALLONS-Y (1)

Music by David Gilmour

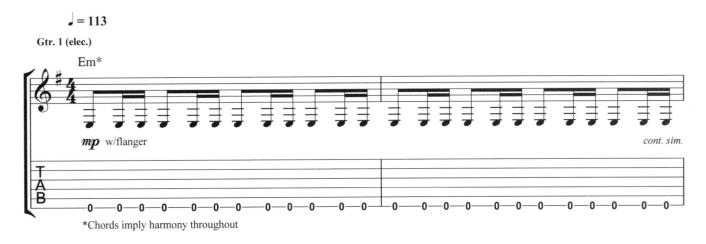

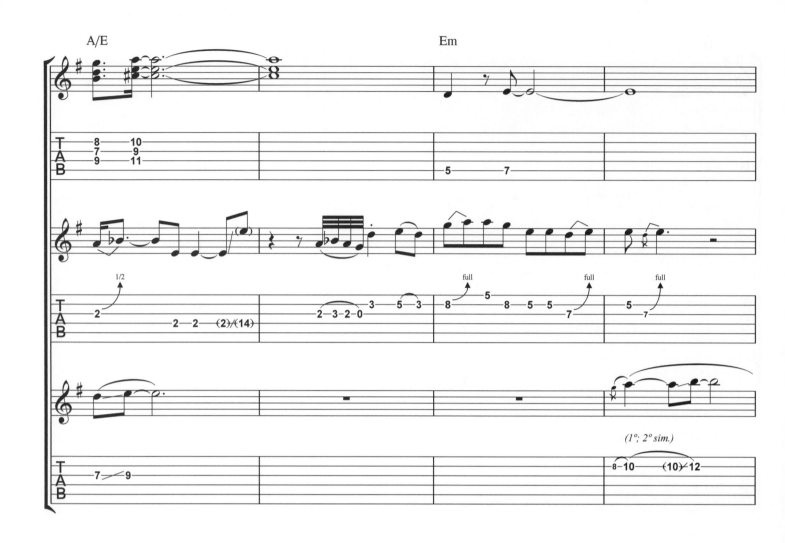

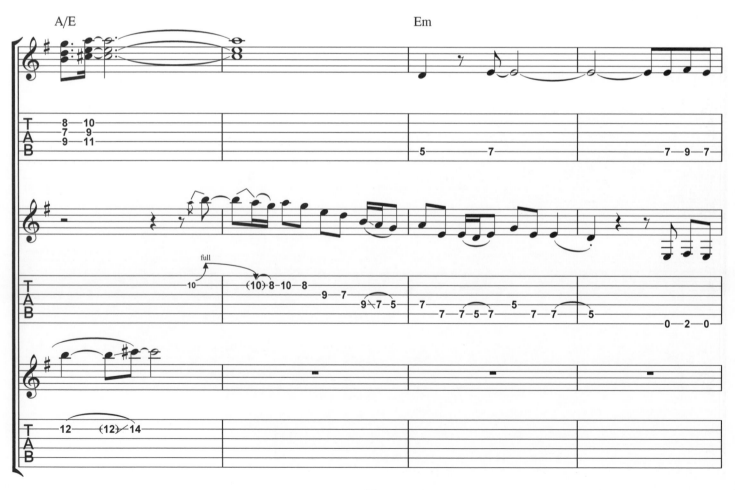

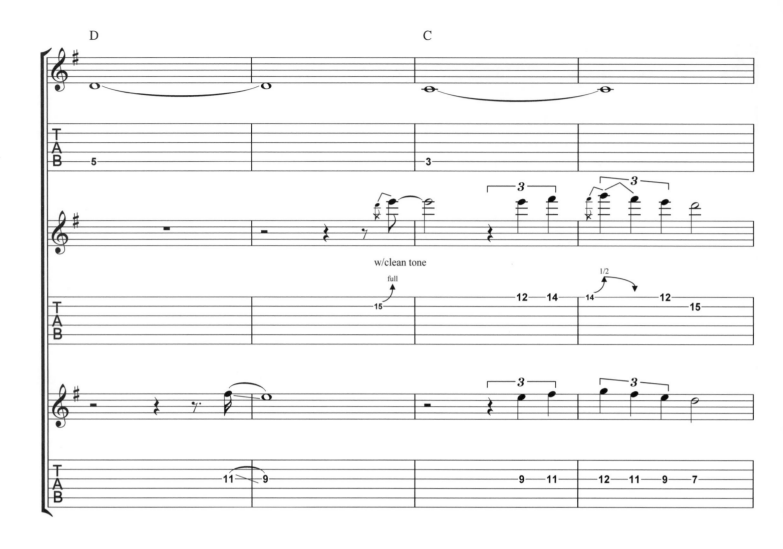

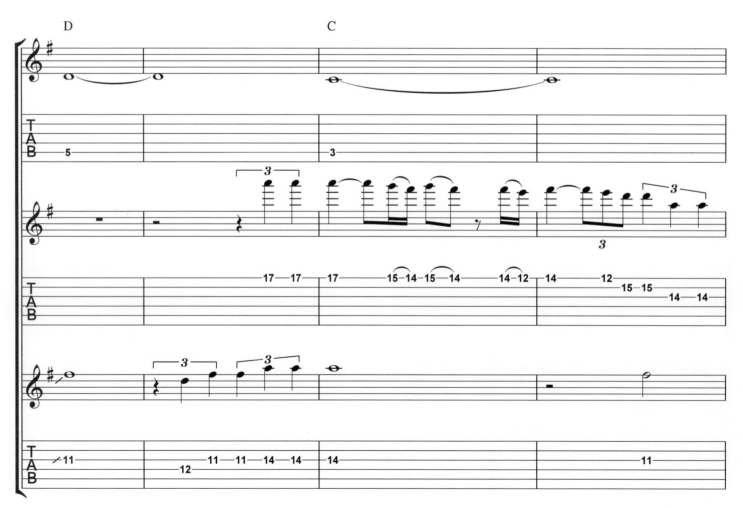

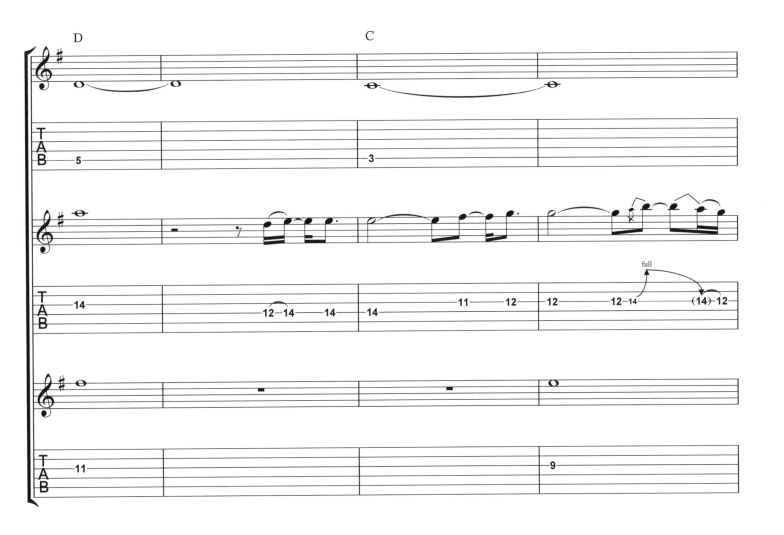

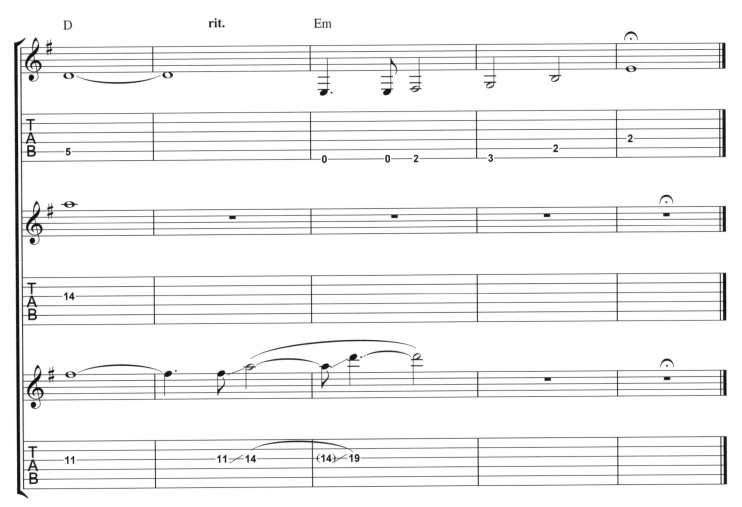

AUTUMN '68

Music by Richard Wright

ALLONS-Y (2)

Music by David Gilmour

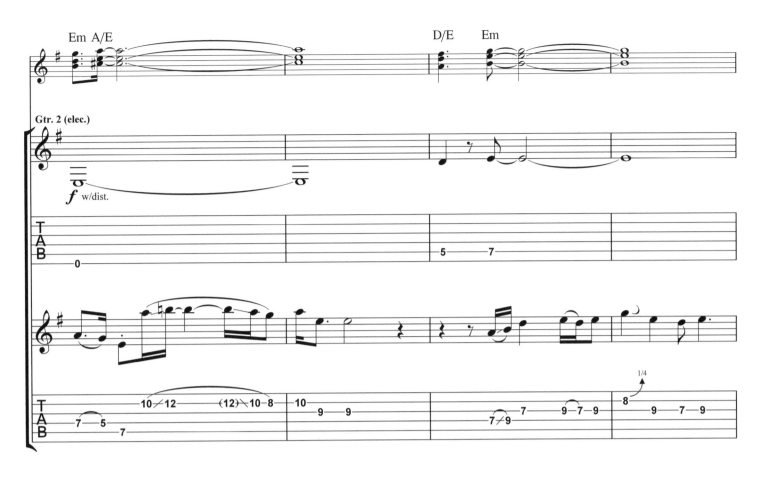

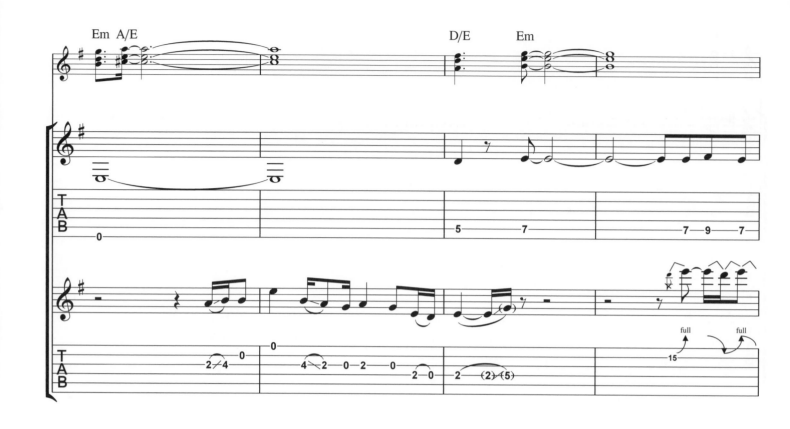

TALKIN' HAWKIN'

Music by David Gilmour & Richard Wright

*Chord names reflect piano harmony

Gtr. 1 plays Fig. 1

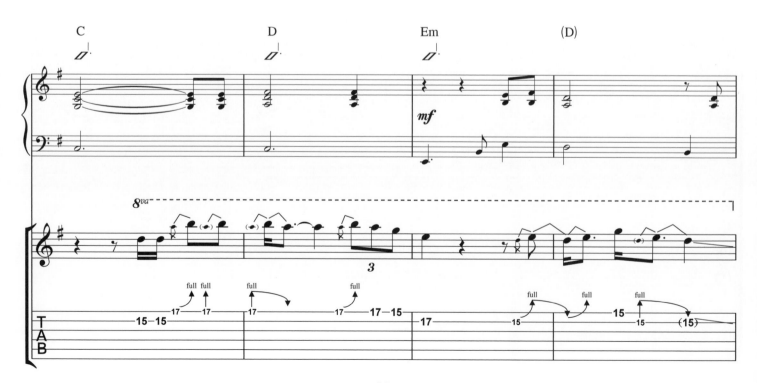

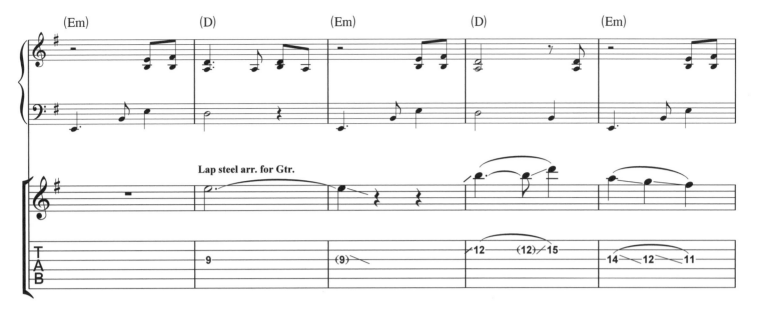

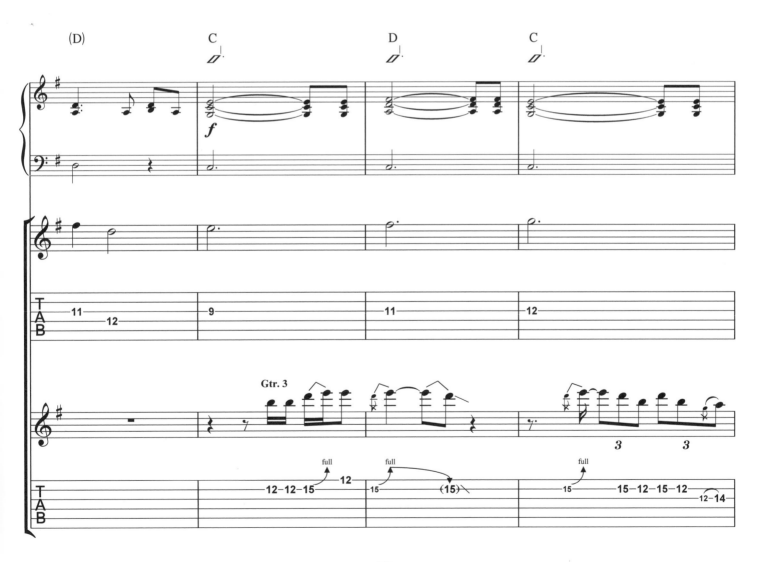

58

Our greatest

hopes could become reality in the future, with the technology at our disposal the possibilities are unbounded.

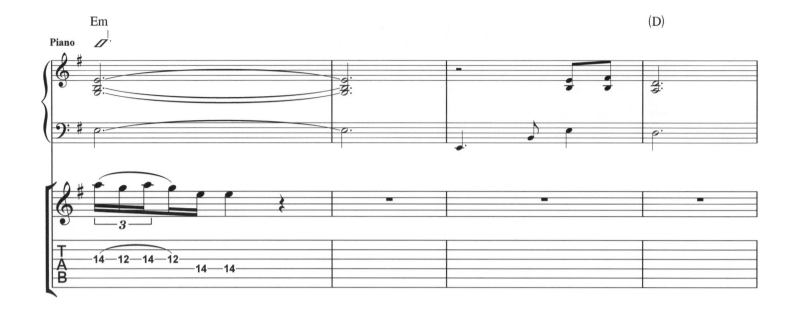

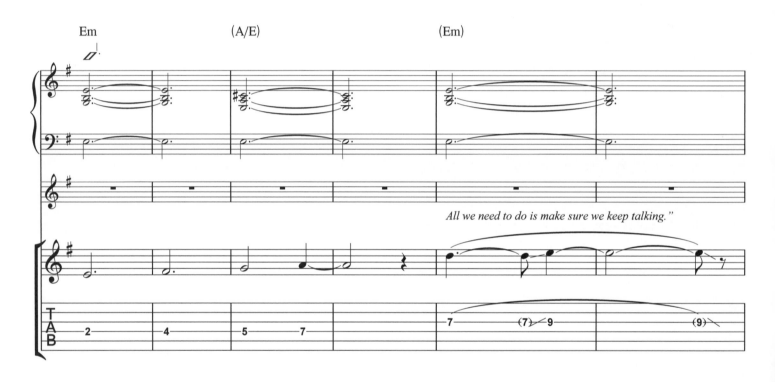

All we need to do is make sure we keep talking."

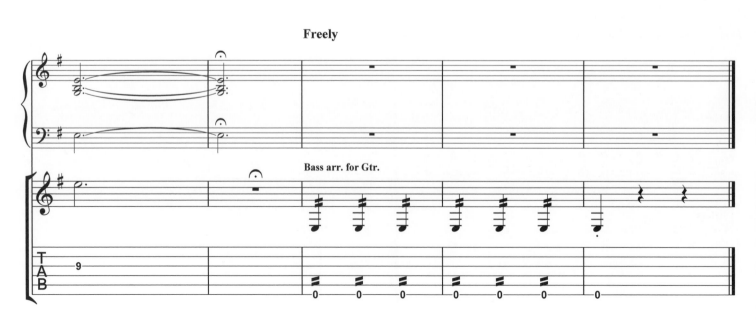

CALLING

Music by David Gilmour & Anthony Moore

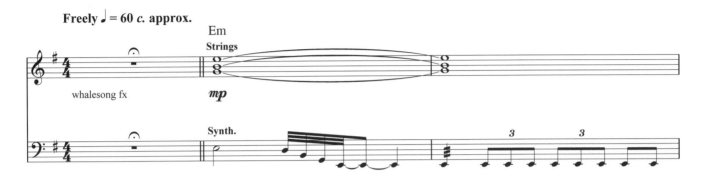

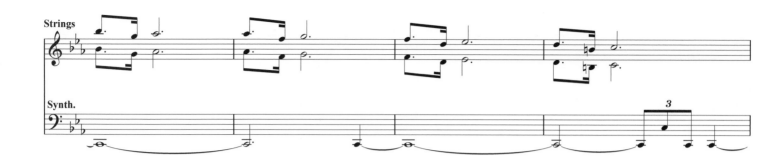

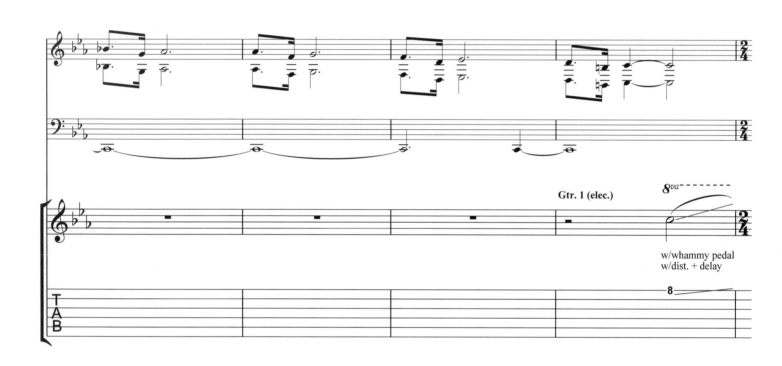

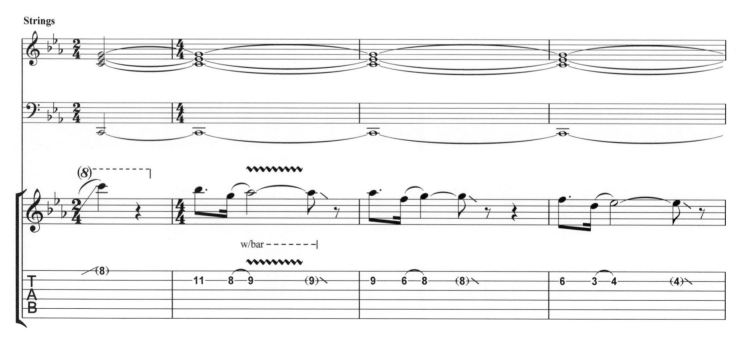

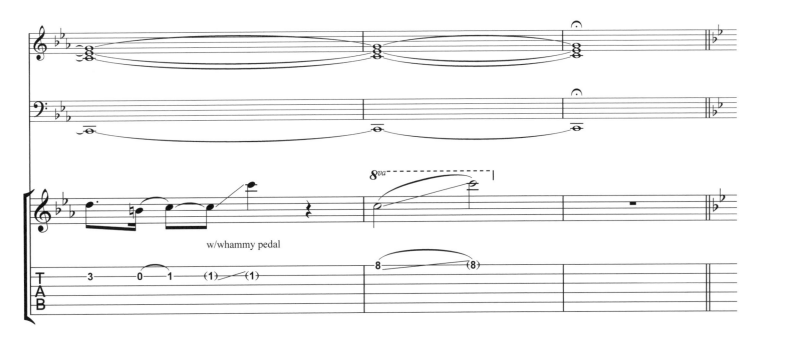

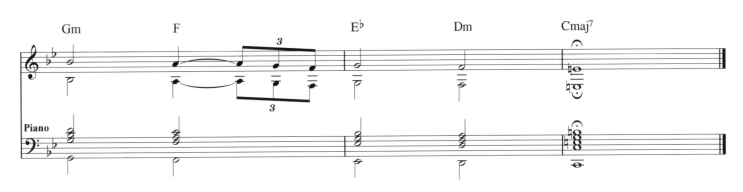

EYES TO PEARLS

Music by David Gilmour

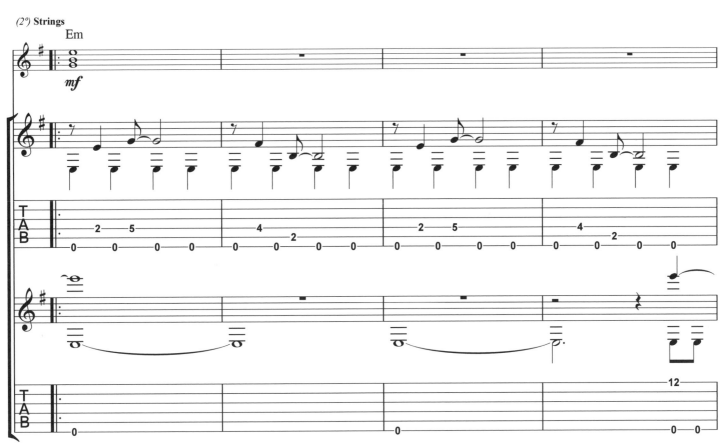

65

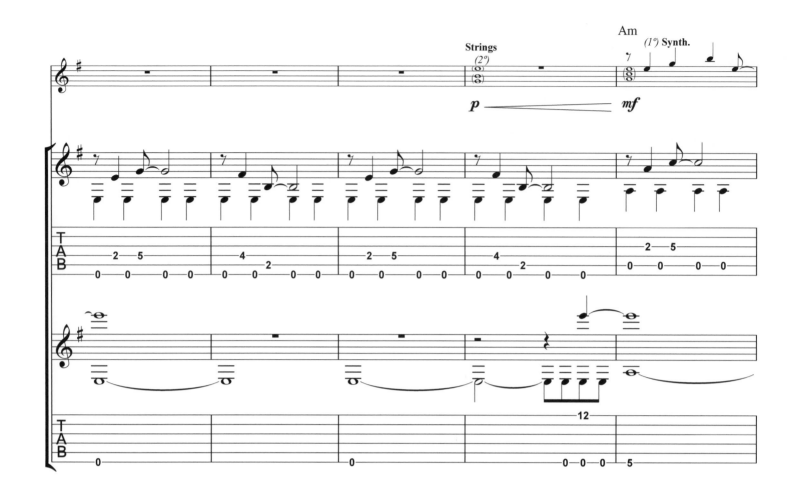

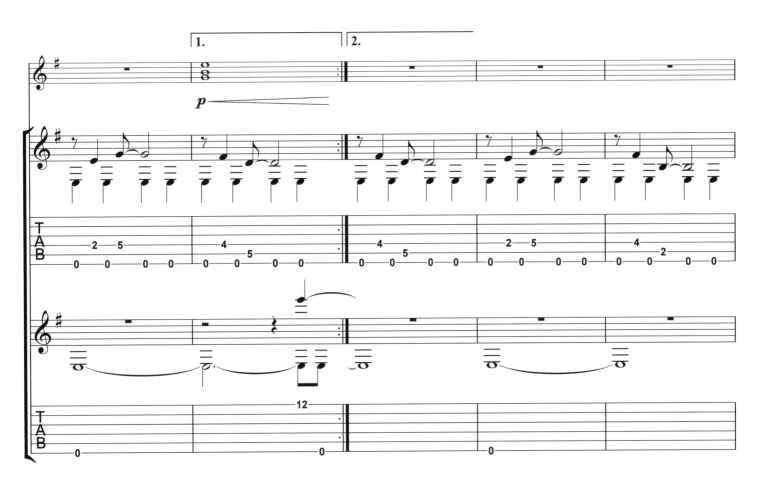

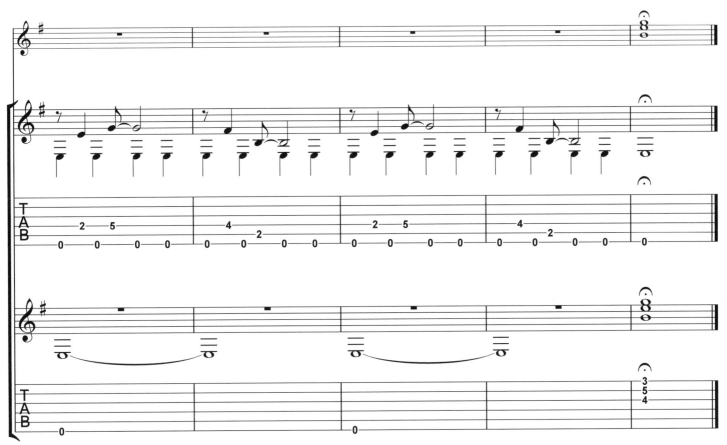

SURFACING

Music by David Gilmour

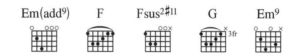

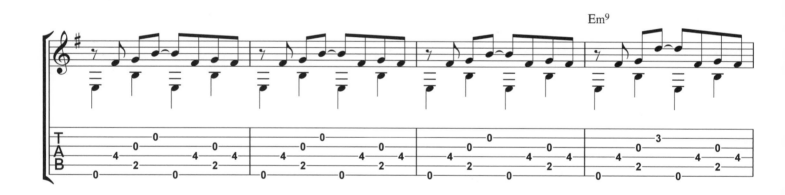

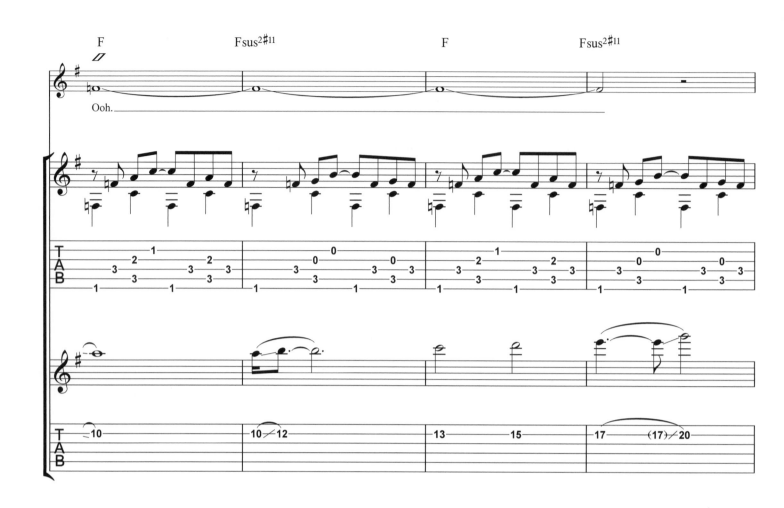

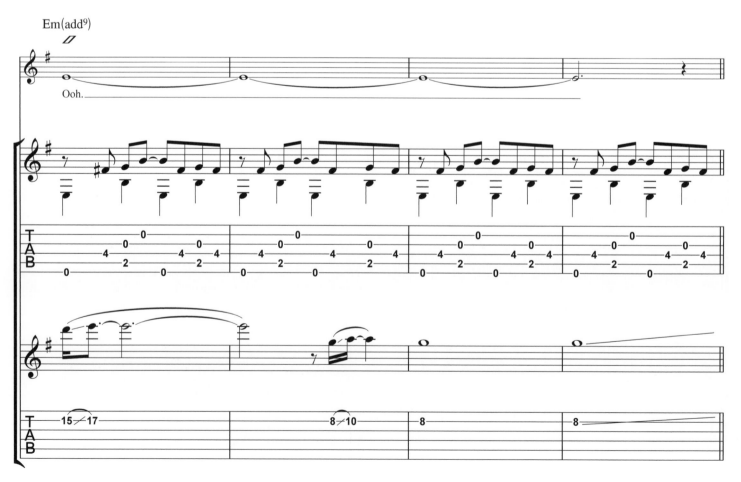

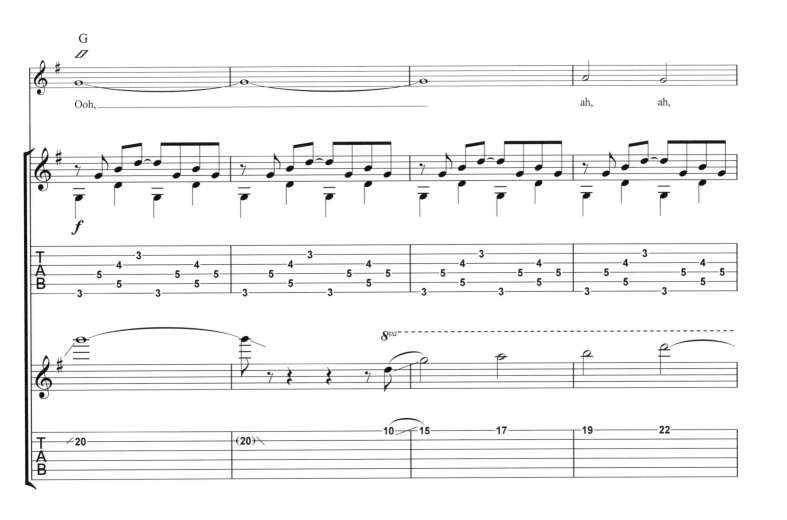

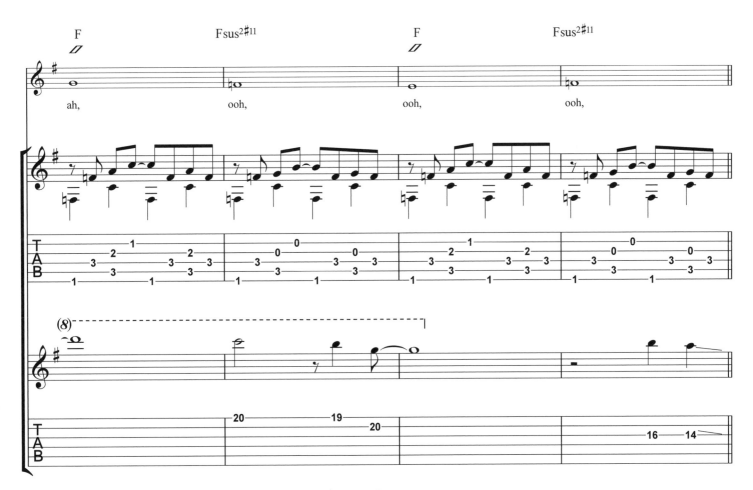

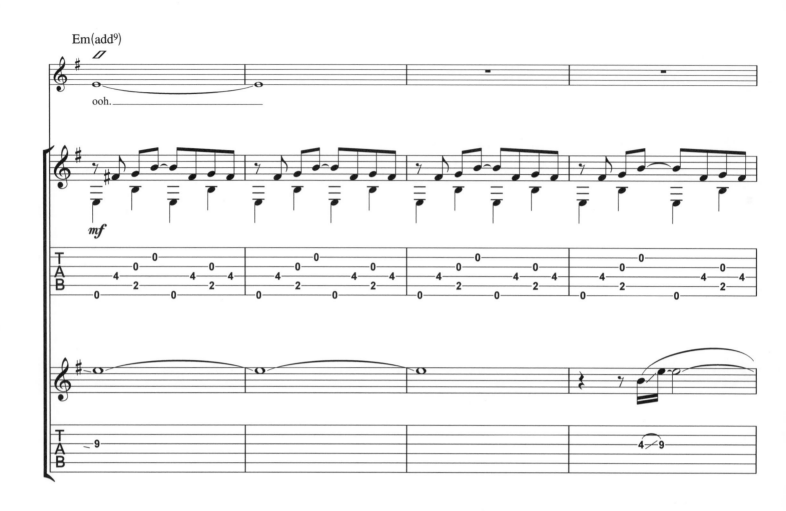

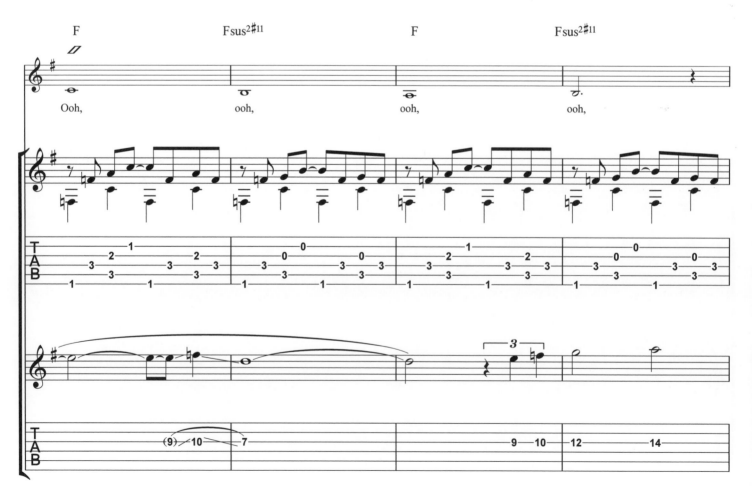

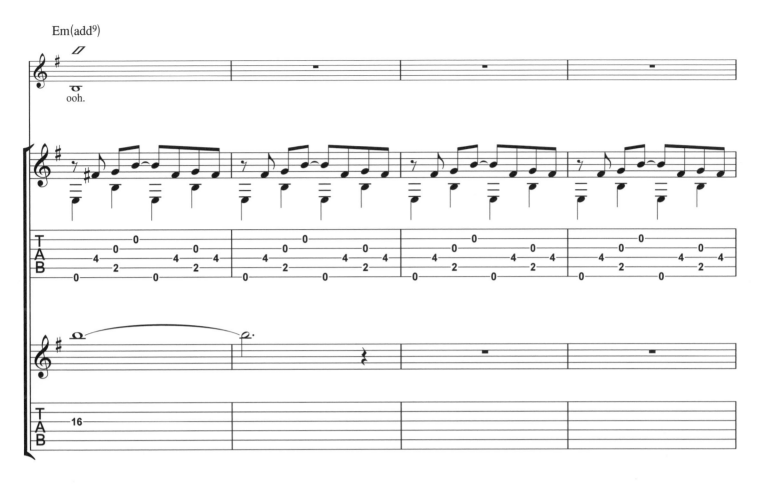

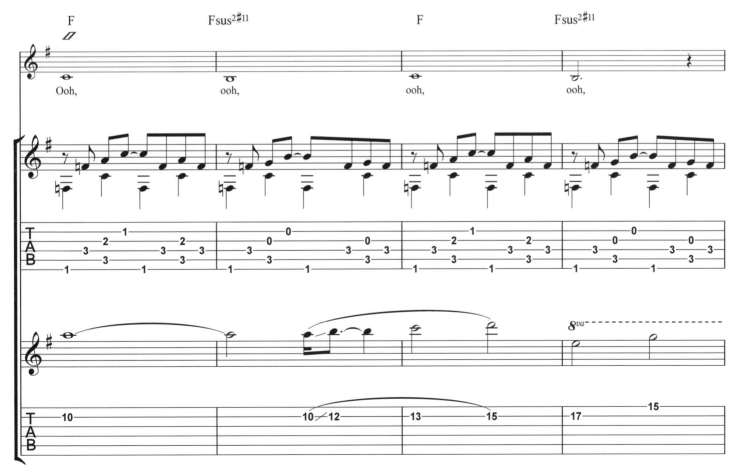

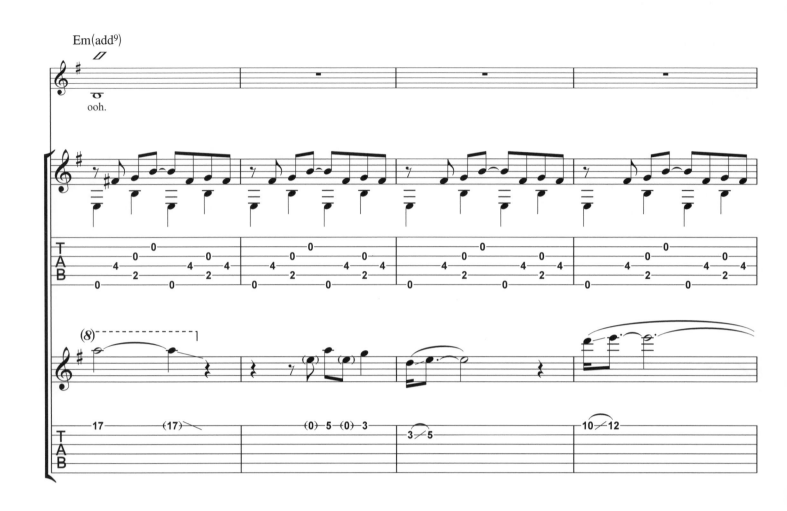

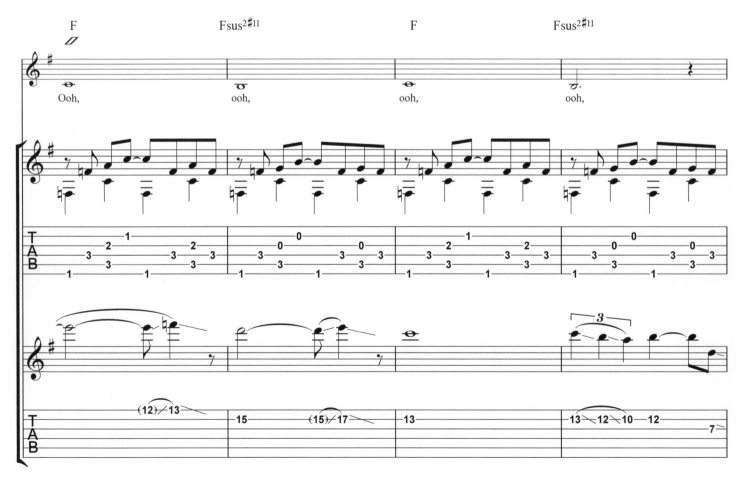

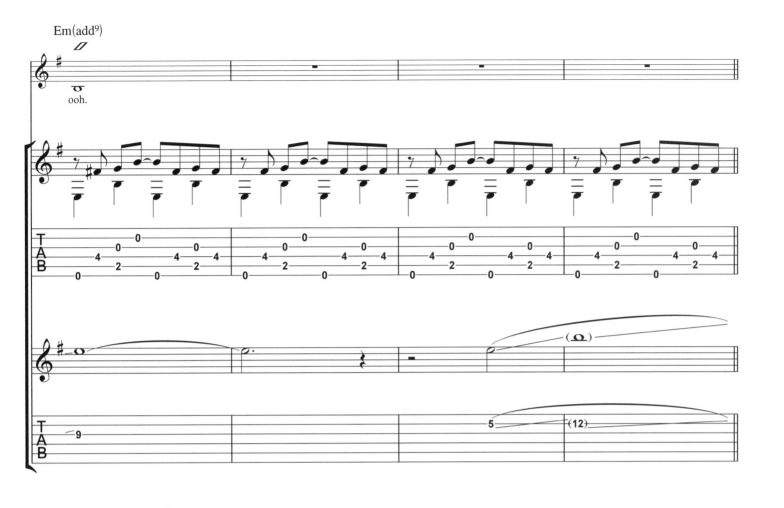

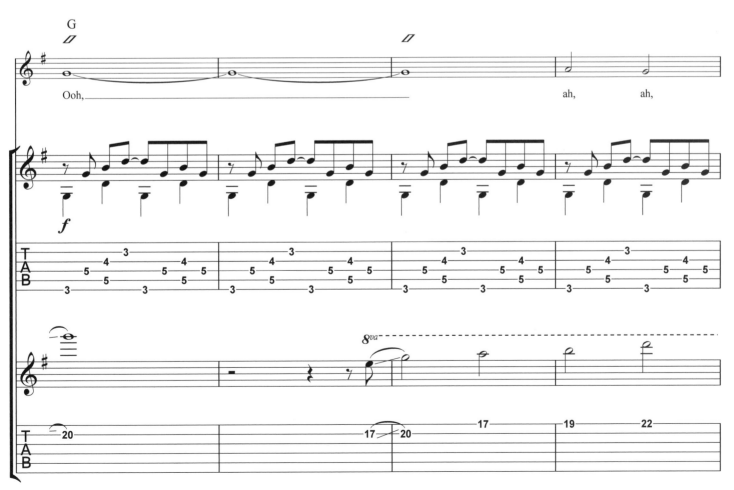

LOUDER THAN WORDS

Music by David Gilmour / Lyrics by Polly Samson

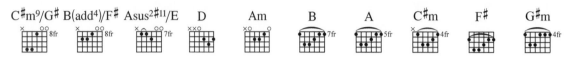

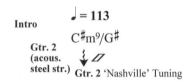

Gtrs. 2+3 are tuned to 'Nashville' tuning: the lowest four strings are replaced with the octave strings from a 12-string set, so they sound an octave higher than normal.

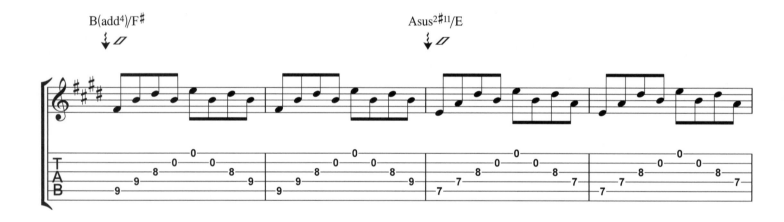

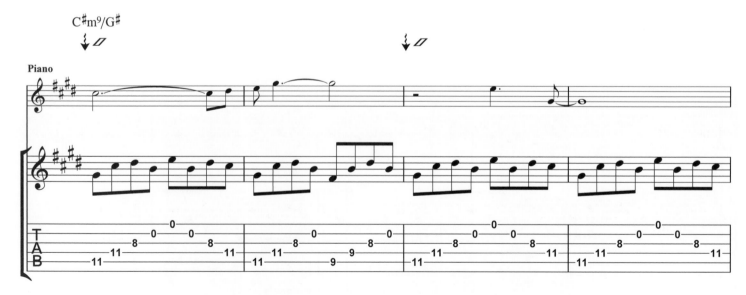

80

These times_ to - ge - ther, rain or shine or stor - my wea - ther,_ this thing_

Gtr. 3 plays Fig. 1

_ we_ do._

Gtr. 4

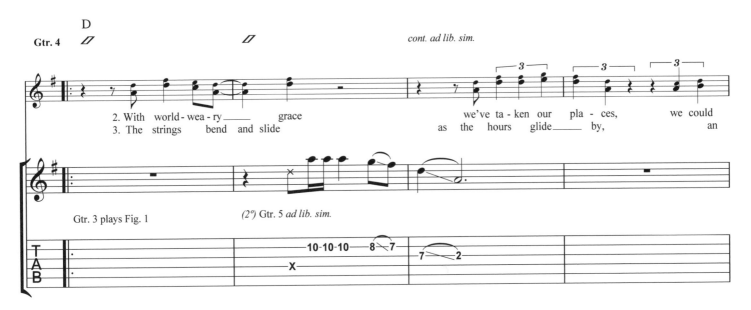

2. With world - wea - ry_ grace we've ta - ken our pla - ces, we could
3. The strings bend and slide as the hours glide_ by, an

Gtr. 3 plays Fig. 1

(2°) Gtr. 5 ad lib. sim.

Loud - er than words.

Loud - er than words,

this thing they call soul is there with a pulse,___ loud - er than words.___

Gtr. 3

cont. in stave

Loud - er than words.___

Gtr. 1

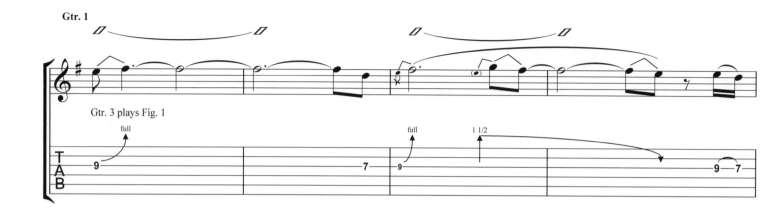

Gtr. 3 plays Fig. 1

Am

D

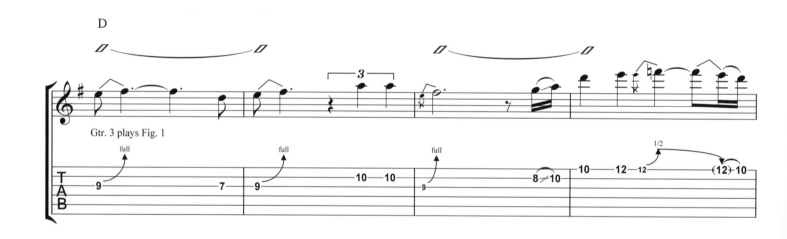

Gtr. 3 plays Fig. 1

Am

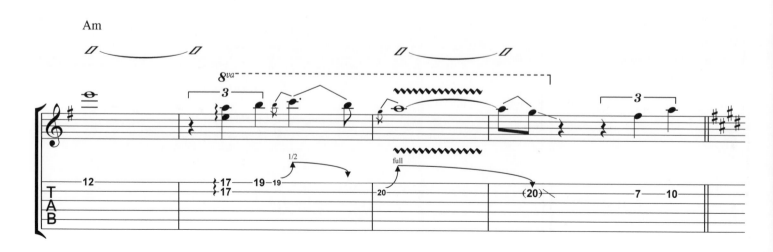

GUITAR TABLATURE EXPLAINED

Guitar music can be explained in three different ways: on a musical stave, in tablature, and in rhythm slashes.

RHYTHM SLASHES: are written above the stave. Strum chords in the rhythm indicated. Round noteheads indicate single notes.

THE MUSICAL STAVE: shows pitches and rhythms and is divided by lines into bars. Pitches are named after the first seven letters of the alphabet.

TABLATURE: graphically represents the guitar fingerboard. Each horizontal line represents a string, and each number represents a fret.

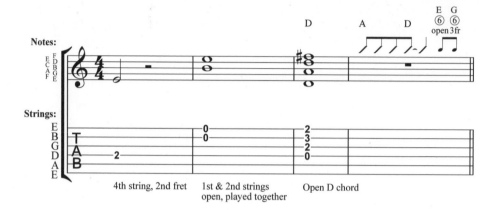

4th string, 2nd fret   1st & 2nd strings open, played together   Open D chord

Definitions for special guitar notation

SEMI-TONE BEND: Strike the note and bend up a semi-tone (½ step).

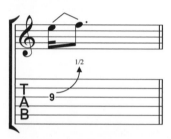

WHOLE-TONE BEND: Strike the note and bend up a whole-tone (full step).

GRACE NOTE BEND: Strike the note and bend as indicated. Play the first note as quickly as possible.

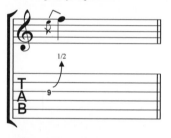

QUARTER-TONE BEND: Strike the note and bend up a ¼ step

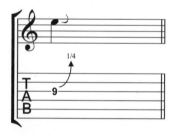

BEND & RELEASE: Strike the note and bend up as indicated, then release back to the original note.

COMPOUND BEND & RELEASE: Strike the note and bend up and down in the rhythm indicated.

PRE-BEND: Bend the note as indicated, then strike it.

PRE-BEND & RELEASE: Bend the note as indicated. Strike it and release the note back to the original pitch.

HAMMER-ON: Strike the first note with one finger, then sound the second note (on the same string) with another finger by fretting it without picking.

PULL-OFF: Place both fingers on the note to be sounded, strike the first note and without picking, pull the finger off to sound the second note.

LEGATO SLIDE (GLISS): Strike the first note and then slide the same fret-hand finger up or down to the second note. The second note is not struck.

MUFFLED STRINGS: A percussive sound is produced by laying the first hand across the string(s) without depressing, and striking them with the pick hand.

TRILL: Very rapidly alternate between the notes indicated by continuously hammering-on and pulling-off.

TREMOLO PICKING: The note is picked as rapidly and continously as possible.

ARPEGGIATE: Play the notes of the chord indicated by quickly rolling them from bottom to top.

SHIFT SLIDE (GLISS & RESTRIKE) Same as legato slide, except the second note is struck.